KU-515-125

THIS WHERE'S WALLY? BOOK BELONGS TO:
HEY, WALLY FANS! FIVE INTREPID TRAVELLERS ARE LOST IN EVERY SCENE! CAN YOU FIND THEM?
ODLAW
WIZARD WHITEBEARD
WENDA
WOOF
WALLY
AND IN EVERY SCENE, THE TRAVELLERS HAVE EACH LOST SOMETHING PRECIOUS! CAN YOU FIND THEM TOO?
WALLY'S KEY
WOOF'S BONE
WENDA'S CAMERA
WIZARD WHITEBEARD'S SCROLL
ODLAW'S BINOCULARS

For my parents

First published 1988 by Walker Books Ltd
87 Vauxhall Walk, London SE11 5HJ

This World Book Day edition published 2012

2 4 6 8 10 9 7 5 3 1

© 1988, 1994, 1997, 2007 Martin Handford

The right of Martin Handford to be identified as author/illustrator
of this work has been asserted by him in accordance with the
Copyright, Designs and Patents Act 1988.

This book has been typeset in Wallyfont and Optima

Printed and bound in China by C&C Offset Printing Co Ltd

All rights reserved.

British Library Cataloguing in Publication Data:
a catalogue record for this book
is available from the British Library.

ISBN 978-1-4063-3905-5

www.walker.co.uk

WHERE'S WALLY NOW?

MARTIN HANDFORD

WALKER BOOKS
AND SUBSIDIARIES
LONDON • BOSTON • SYDNEY • AUCKLAND

THE ABSOLUTELY HUGE AND ENORMOUSLY INTERESTING BOOK OF CAVEMEN,
CAVE WOMEN, CAVE DOGS AND ALL SORTS OF EXTREMELY SAVAGE STONE-AGE BEASTS.
HI THERE, BOOK WORMS!
SOME BITS OF HISTORY ARE AMAZING! I SIT HERE READING ALL THESE BOOKS ABOUT THE WORLD LONG AGO, AND IT'S LIKE RIDING A TIME MACHINE. WHY NOT TRY IT FOR YOURSELVES? JUST SEARCH EACH PICTURE AND FIND ME, WOOF (REMEMBER, ALL YOU CAN SEE IS HIS TAIL), WENDA, WIZARD WHITEBEARD AND ODLAW. THEN LOOK FOR MY KEY, WOOF'S BONE (IN THIS SCENE IT'S THE BONE THAT'S NEAREST TO HIS TAIL), WENDA'S CAMERA, WIZARD WHITEBEARD'S SCROLL AND ODLAW'S BINOCULARS.
THERE ARE ALSO 25 WALLY-WATCHERS, EACH OF WHOM APPEARS ONLY ONCE SOMEWHERE ON MY TRAVELS. AND ONE MORE THING! CAN YOU FIND ANOTHER CHARACTER, NOT SHOWN BELOW, WHO APPEARS ONCE IN EVERY PICTURE?
Wally

4,578 YEARS AGO
THE RIDDLE OF THE PYRAMIDS
THE ANCIENT EGYPTIANS WERE VERY CLEVER PEOPLE WHO LOVED GODS, CATS AND SPHINX, AND INVENTED PYRAMIDS. WITH GREAT SKILL AND HARD WORK THEY BUILT HUGE WONDERS IN THE DESERT.
BUT FOR HUNDREDS OF YEARS MANY PEOPLE WERE PUZZLED BY THEM. WHAT WERE THEY FOR? WHY WERE THEY SO BIG?
WHY WERE THEY THAT SHAPE? WAS IT POSSIBLE (OR EVEN LIKELY) THAT PHARAOHS WERE BURIED UNDER THEM? THESE MAGNIFICENT MONUMENTS ARE STILL AMAZING PEOPLE TO THIS DAY.

2,000 YEARS AGO
FVN AND GAMES IN ANCIENT ROME
THE ROMANS SPENT MOST OF THEIR TIME FIGHTING, CONQVERING, LEARNING LATIN AND MAKING ROADS. WHEN THEY TOOK THEIR HOLIDAYS THEY ALWAYS HAD GAMES AT THE COLISEVM (AN OLD SORT OF PLAYGROVND). THEIR FAVOURITE GAMES WERE FIGHTING, MORE FIGHTING, CHARIOT RACING, FIGHTING AND FEEDING CHRISTIANS TO LIONS. WHEN THE CROWD GAVE A GLADIATOR THE THVMBS DOWN IT MEANT KILL YOUR OPPONENT. THVMBS UP MEANT LET HIM GO, TO FIGHT TO THE DEATH ANOTHER DAY.

1,003 YEARS AGO
ON TOUR WITH THE VIKINGS
At home the Vikings were quiet people, who liked knitting and cheese tasting and boring things like that. But on tour they went wild. They put on their best horned hats and sailed across the sea, singing and shouting like mad. If you heard them coming, it was best to run away; because once they had arrived and unpacked their axes, there was no holding them back.

800 YEARS AGO

Chaos at the Castle

Castles were built all across Europe and the people living in them often had a beautiful view of the countryside. Unfortunately they might also have had a view of an army laying siege to their castle. Luckily when these besieging armies finally ran out of clean tights and tunics they returned home. For years afterwards the knights told stories of the spectacular castles they had battered and bashed and the fascinating people they had captured – and wondered why they were never invited to parties!

600 YEARS AGO

ONCE UPON A SATURDAY MORNING

The Middle Ages were a very merry time to be alive, especially on Saturdays, as long as you didn't get caught. Short skirts and stripy tights were in fashion for men; everybody knew lots of jokes; there was widespread joggling and jousting and archery and jesting and fun. But if you got into trouble, the Middle Ages could be miserable. For the man in the stocks or the pillory or about to lose his head, Saturday morning was no laughing matter.

171,185 DAYS AGO

THE LAST DAYS OF THE AZTECS

The Aztecs lived in sunny Mexico and were rich and strong and liked swinging from poles pretending to be eagles. They also liked making human sacrifices to their gods, so it was best to agree with everything they said. The Spanish were also rich and strong, and some of them, called conquistadors, came to Mexico in 1519 to have an adventure.

However, when the Aztecs and Spanish met they did not agree on much.

OLD JAPAN
TROUBLE IN
400 YEARS AGO
Is red better than blue? What do you mean, your poem about cherry blossom is better than mine? Shall we have another cup of tea? Over difficult questions such as these, the Japanese fought fiercely for hundreds of years. The fiercest fighters of all were the samurai, who wore flags on their backs so that their mummies could find them. The fighters without flags were called ashigaru. They couldn't take a joke any better than the samurai, especially about not having flags.

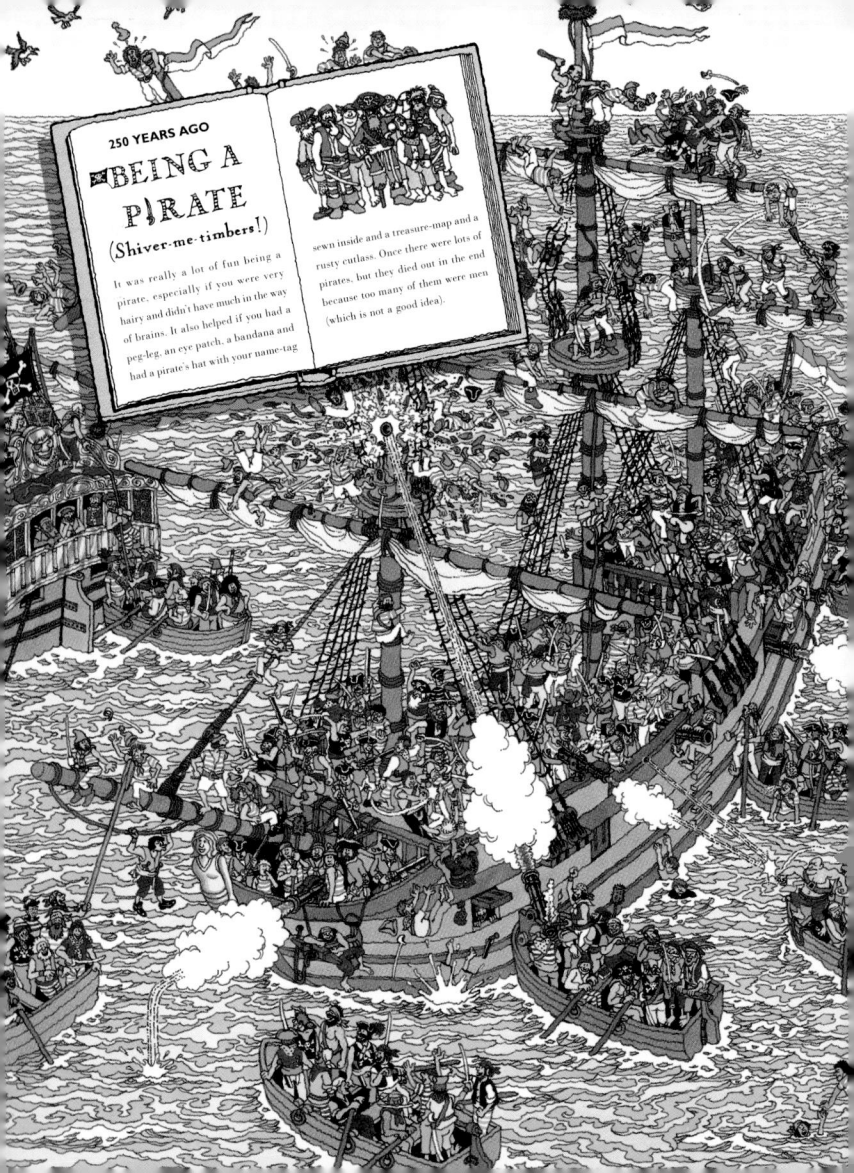
250 YEARS AGO
BEING A PIRATE
(Shiver-me-timbers!)
It was really a lot of fun being a pirate, especially if you were very hairy and didn't have much in the way of brains. It also helped if you had a peg-leg, an eye patch, a bandana and had a pirate's hat with your name-tag sewn inside and a treasure-map and a rusty cutlass. Once there were lots of pirates, but they died out in the end because too many of them were men (which is not a good idea).

MORE THAN 100 YEARS AGO
HAVING A BALL
IN GAYE PARÉE
The history of France has some very bad bits, like getting your head chopped off by Madame Guillotine in the French Revolution; and some very good bits, like the invention of smelly cheese. In 1870 Napoleon (the third one) threw a marvellous ball in Paris to celebrate 1870 being a good bit. All the beautiful people came and danced the night away to a band called the Third Republic.

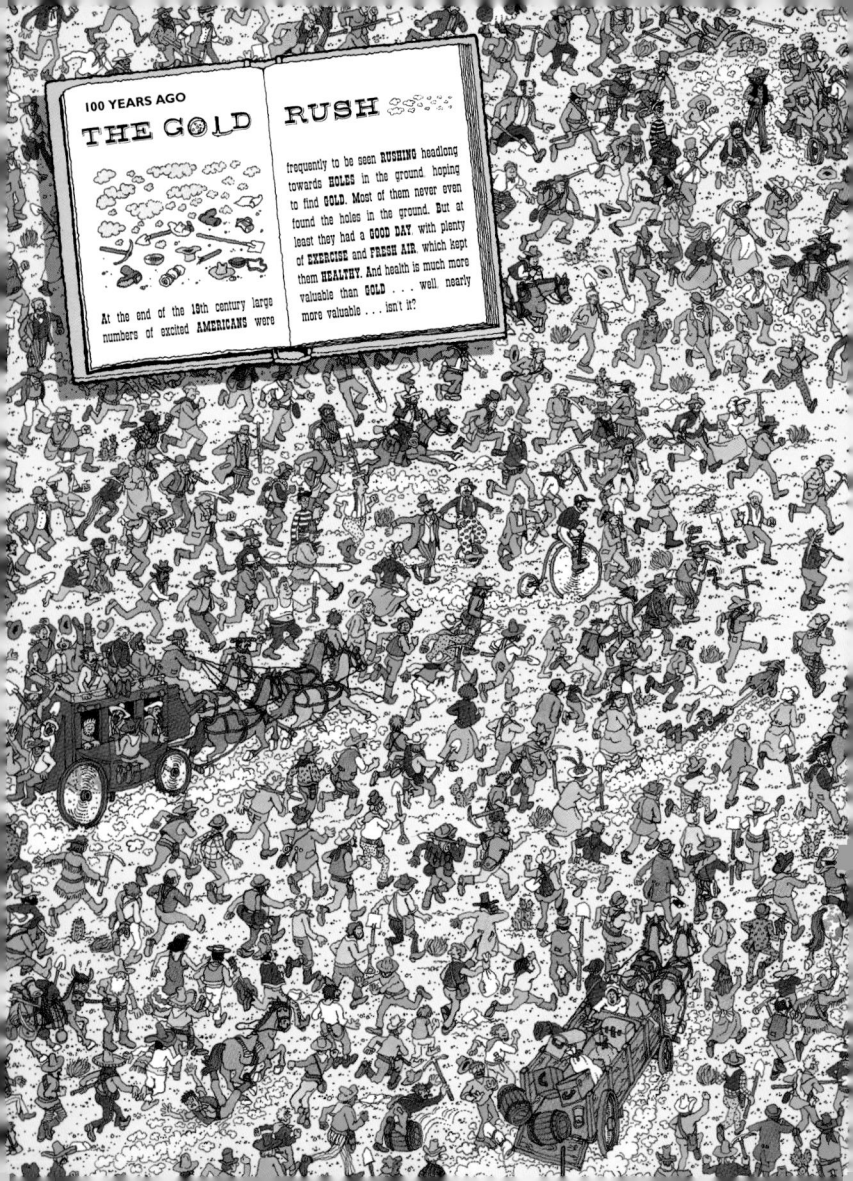

100 YEARS AGO

THE GOLD RUSH

At the end of the 19th century large numbers of excited **AMERICANS** were frequently to be seen **RUSHING** headlong towards **HOLES** in the ground, hoping to find **GOLD**. Most of them never even found the holes in the ground. But at least they had a **GOOD DAY**, with plenty of **EXERCISE** and **FRESH AIR**, which kept them **HEALTHY**. And health is much more valuable than **GOLD** . . . well, nearly more valuable . . . isn't it?

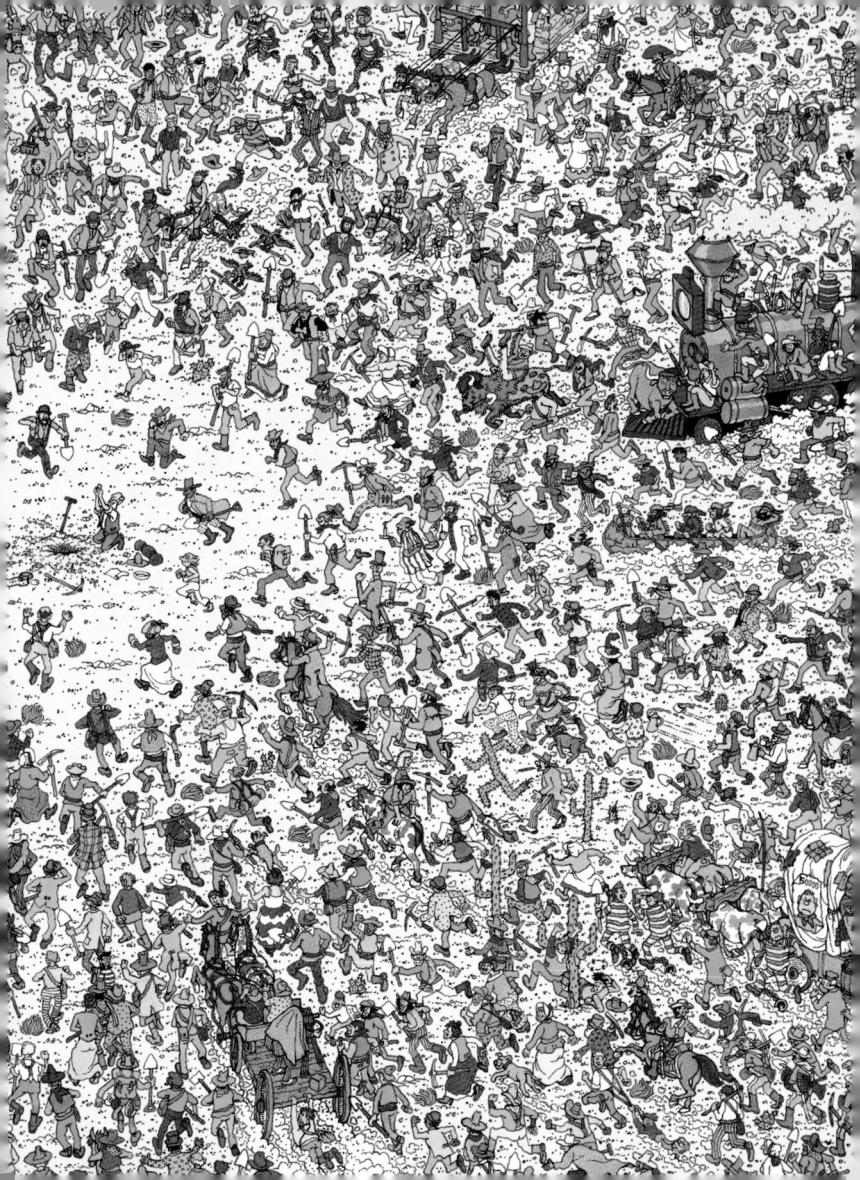

WALLY IS LOST IN THE FUTURE! FIND HIM! RESCUE HIM! WALLY'S BOOKS ARE LOST IN THE PAST! FIND THEM! RESCUE THEM! THERE'S ONE LOST IN EACH PICTURE. GO BACK AND LOOK FOR THEM! WHERE'S WALLY?
WHERE'S WALLY NOW?

THE GREAT WHERE'S WALLY NOW? CHECKLIST

Hundreds more things for time travellers to look for!

THE STONE AGE

- [ ] Four cavemen swinging into trouble
- [ ] An accident with an axe
- [ ] A great invention
- [ ] A Stone-age rodeo
- [ ] Boars chasing a man
- [ ] Men chasing a boar
- [ ] Seven fish
- [ ] A mammoth squirt
- [ ] A romantic caveman and cavewomen
- [ ] A bear trap
- [ ] A mammoth in the river
- [ ] A fruit stall
- [ ] Charging woolly rhinos
- [ ] A big cover-up
- [ ] A trunk holding a trunk
- [ ] A knockout game of baseball
- [ ] A rocky picture show
- [ ] An upside-down boar
- [ ] A spoilt dog
- [ ] A lesson on dinosaurs
- [ ] A very scruffy family
- [ ] Some dangerous spear fishermen

THE RIDDLE OF THE PYRAMIDS

- [ ] An upside-down pyramid
- [ ] A Pharaoh choosing a sarcophagus
- [ ] A little boy helping to paint a mural
- [ ] Dates falling from a tree
- [ ] A chariot racer without his chariot
- [ ] Men carrying a mural in a mural
- [ ] Eight protruding tongues
- [ ] Stones defying gravity
- [ ] Six workers pushing a block of stone
- [ ] Someone wearing a red cloak
- [ ] Two assistants mixing paint
- [ ] A thirsty sphinx
- [ ] A runaway block of stone
- [ ] Nine shields
- [ ] Someone blowing a horn
- [ ] A picture firing an arrow
- [ ] Three water-carriers
- [ ] Sunbathers in peril
- [ ] A messy milking session
- [ ] A contented animal being stroked
- [ ] Pyramids of sand

FUN AND GAMES IN ANCIENT ROME

- [ ] A charioteer who has lost his chariot
- [ ] Coliseum cleaners
- [ ] An unequal contest with spears
- [ ] A winner who is about to lose
- [ ] A lion with good table manners
- [ ] A deadly set of wheels
- [ ] Lion cubs being teased
- [ ] Four shields that match their owners
- [ ] A pyramid of lions
- [ ] Lions giving the paws down
- [ ] A leopard chasing a leopard skin
- [ ] A piggyback puncher
- [ ] An awful musician
- [ ] A painful fork-lift
- [ ] A horse holding the reins
- [ ] A leopard in love
- [ ] A roman keeping count
- [ ] A gladiator losing his sandals

ON TOUR WITH THE VIKINGS

- [ ] A happy figurehead
- [ ] Figureheads in love
- [ ] A man being used as a club
- [ ] A tearful sheep
- [ ] Two hopeless hiding places
- [ ] Childish Vikings
- [ ] A beard with a foot on it
- [ ] An eagle posing as a helmet
- [ ] A sailor tearing a sail
- [ ] A heavily armed Viking
- [ ] A patchy couple
- [ ] Three spearheads being lopped off
- [ ] A burning behind
- [ ] A bending boat
- [ ] Three startled figureheads
- [ ] Locked horns
- [ ] A helmet with a spider
- [ ] A helmet of smoke
- [ ] A bullfight

CHAOS AT THE CASTLE

- [ ] A soldier getting the point
- [ ] A man about to be catapulted
- [ ] A human bridge
- [ ] A key that's out of reach
- [ ] A message for the milkman
- [ ] A cauldron of boiling oil
- [ ] A battering-man
- [ ] Two hands gripping a soldier's arms
- [ ] A load of washing
- [ ] Two catapult catastrophes
- [ ] A catapult aiming the wrong way
- [ ] A shower of spears
- [ ] A soldier fast asleep
- [ ] A ladder which is too short
- [ ] Flattened soldiers
- [ ] Rockfaces
- [ ] Attackers in the wrong colour stripes
- [ ] A ticklish situation

ONCE UPON A SATURDAY MORNING

- [ ] A dirty downpour
- [ ] Archers missing the target
- [ ] A jouster sitting back to front
- [ ] A dog stalking a cat stalking some birds
- [ ] A long line of pickpockets
- [ ] A jouster who needs lots of practice
- [ ] A man making a bear dance
- [ ] A bear making a man dance
- [ ] Hats that are tied together
- [ ] Fruit and vegetable thieves
- [ ] An unexpected puddle
- [ ] A juggling jester
- [ ] A very long drink
- [ ] A heavily burdened beast
- [ ] A gentleman kissing a lady's hand
- [ ] A man scything hats
- [ ] An angry fish
- [ ] A ticklish torture
- [ ] Minstrels making an awful noise

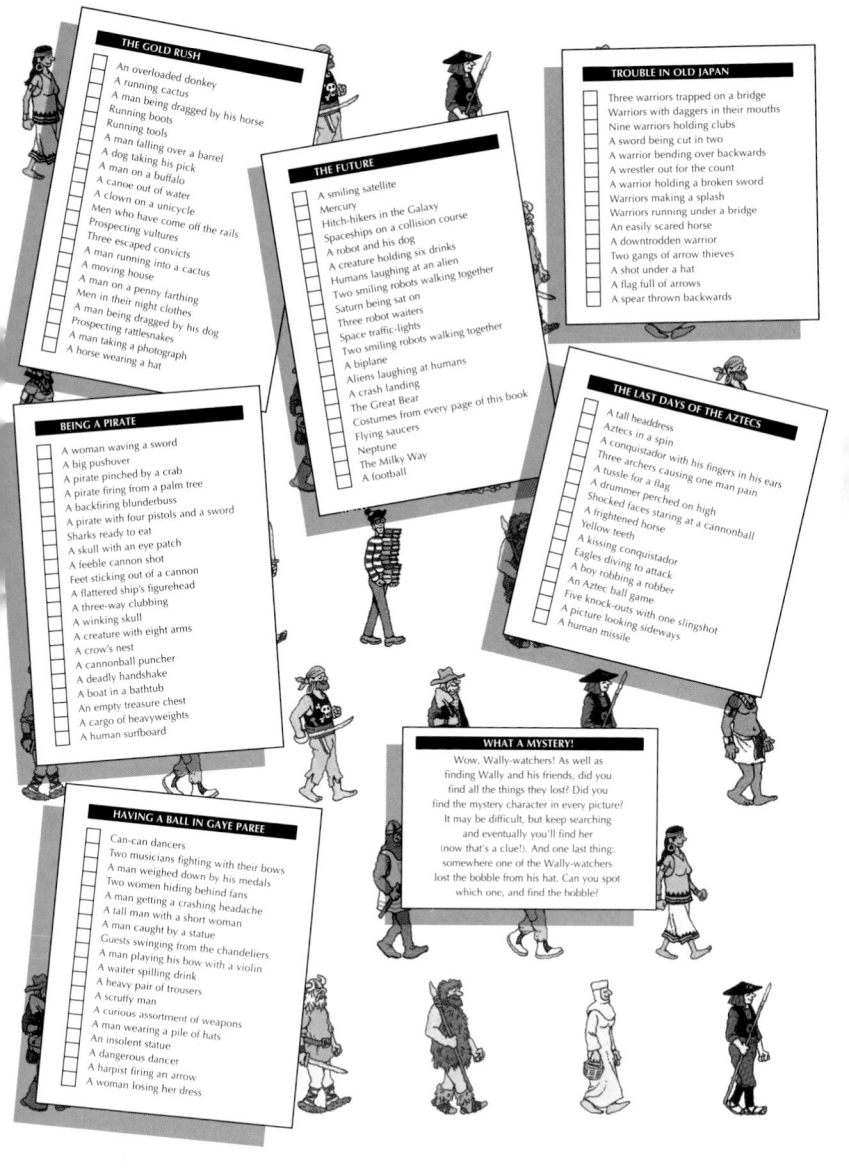

THE GOLD RUSH

- An overloaded donkey
- A running cactus
- A man being dragged by his horse
- Running boots
- Running tools
- A man falling over a barrel
- A dog taking his pick
- A man on a buffalo
- A canoe out of water
- A clown on a unicycle
- Men who have come off the rails
- Prospecting vultures
- Three escaped convicts
- A man running into a cactus
- A moving house
- A man on a penny farthing
- Men in their night clothes
- A man being dragged by his dog
- Prospecting rattlesnakes
- A man taking a photograph
- A horse wearing a hat

THE FUTURE

- A smiling satellite
- Mercury
- Hitch-hikers in the Galaxy
- Spaceships on a collision course
- A robot and his dog
- A creature holding six drinks
- Humans laughing at an alien
- Two smiling robots walking together
- Saturn being sat on
- Three robot waiters
- Space traffic-lights
- Two smiling robots walking together
- A biplane
- Aliens laughing at humans
- A crash landing
- The Great Bear
- Costumes from every page of this book
- Flying saucers
- Neptune
- The Milky Way
- A football

TROUBLE IN OLD JAPAN

- Three warriors trapped on a bridge
- Warriors with daggers in their mouths
- Nine warriors holding clubs
- A sword being cut in two
- A warrior bending over backwards
- A wrestler out for the count
- A warrior holding a broken sword
- Warriors making a splash
- Warriors running under a bridge
- An easily scared horse
- A downtrodden warrior
- Two gangs of arrow thieves
- A shot under a hat
- A flag full of arrows
- A spear thrown backwards

BEING A PIRATE

- A woman waving a sword
- A big pushover
- A pirate pinched by a crab
- A pirate firing from a palm tree
- A backfiring blunderbuss
- A pirate with four pistols and a sword
- Sharks ready to eat
- A skull with an eye patch
- A feeble cannon shot
- Feet sticking out of a cannon
- A flattered ship's figurehead
- A three-way clubbing
- A winking skull
- A creature with eight arms
- A crow's nest
- A cannonball puncher
- A deadly handshake
- A boat in a bathtub
- An empty treasure chest
- A cargo of heavyweights
- A human surfboard

THE LAST DAYS OF THE AZTECS

- A tall headdress
- Aztecs in a spin
- A conquistador with his fingers in his ears
- Three archers causing one man pain
- A tussle for a flag
- A drummer perched on high
- Shocked faces staring at a cannonball
- A frightened horse
- Yellow teeth
- A kissing conquistador
- Eagles diving to attack
- A boy robbing a robber
- An Aztec ball game
- Five knock-outs with one slingshot
- A picture-looking sideways
- A human missile

WHAT A MYSTERY!

Wow, Wally-watchers! As well as finding Wally and his friends, did you find all the things they lost? Did you find the mystery character in every picture? It may be difficult, but keep searching and eventually you'll find her (now that's a clue!). And one last thing: somewhere one of the Wally-watchers lost the bobble from his hat. Can you spot which one, and find the bobble?

HAVING A BALL IN GAYE PAREE

- Can-can dancers
- Two musicians fighting with their bows
- A man weighed down by his medals
- Two women hiding behind fans
- A man getting a crashing headache
- A tall man with a short woman
- A man caught by a statue
- Guests swinging from the chandeliers
- A man playing his bow with a violin
- A waiter spilling drink
- A heavy pair of trousers
- A scruffy man
- A curious assortment of weapons
- A man wearing a pile of hats
- An insolent statue
- A dangerous dancer
- A harpist firing an arrow
- A woman losing her dress

WHERE'S WALLY?

25 YEARS

Where's Wally? The Search for the Lost Things

Publishing
April 2012

Have *you* found Wally yet?